BILL BOY

BY
MELANIE JOYCE

ILLUSTRATED BY
ANTHONY WILLIAMS

FULL FLIGHT runway

Titles in the FULL FLIGHT ✈ runway » series

Badger Publishing Limited
Suite G08, Business & Technology Centre
Bessemer Drive, Stevenage, Hertfordshire, SG1 2DX
Telephone: 01438 791037   Fax: 01438 791036
www.badger-publishing.co.uk

Billy's Boy ISBN 978 1 84691 847 6

Publisher: David Jamieson
Editor: Danny Pearson
Design: Fiona Grant
Illustration: Anthony Williams
Printed and bound in China through Colorcraft Ltd., Hong Kong

BILLY'S BOY

CONTENTS

Badger Publishing

Vocabulary:

Traveller   Tabbart

Cob   Expresses

Bidding

Main Characters:

Billy

Dad

CHAPTER 1
THE WISH

Billy lives on a Traveller camp.

He wants his own horse.

He goes to talk to his Mother.

She is washing down the trailer.

There is a horse fair in two weeks.

Mum says Billy must ask his Dad.

CHAPTER 2
BOY

At the horse fair, Billy sees a wonderful cob. His name is Boy.

Dad is not sure.

The bidding starts.

Billy is frustrated.

Someone has bid for Boy.

The sale is over.

Billy returns to the camp.

He is bitterly disappointed.

CHAPTER 3
BIRTHDAY BOY

It is Billy's Birthday.

He is in no mood to celebrate.

Everyone in the camp has gathered.

Dad has a surprise for Billy

Dad tells Billy to close his eyes.

He leads him forward.

He hears a soft whinny

Billy opens his eyes.

Boy is by the trailer.

Billy is over the moon.

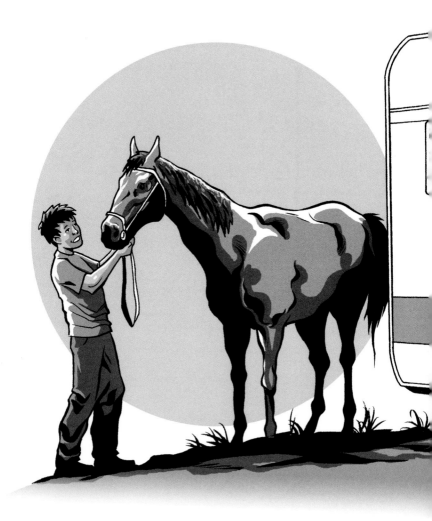

Questions:

Where does Billy live?

Where does Billy and his Dad go to try
and find a horse?

Is Billy surprised that he got Boy
(the horse) for his birthday?

What would you wish for your next
birthday?

Weather Girl

by
Melanie Joyce

illustrated by
Anthony Williams

Contents

Vocabulary:

Weather	Changing
Disappeared	Predict
Park	Rain
Sun	Mad
Snowman	

Main Characters:

Farah is from Iran. She is not used to the weather changing a lot. Ava is her best friend.

Chapter 1
Farah's Diary

I'm fed up with the weather.

One minute it is sunny.

The next minute it is raining.

I never know what to wear.

The weather keeps changing.

I can't keep up.

Chapter 2
The Forecast

Monday

It was sunny this morning.

Later on, the sun disappeared.

Tuesday

I wore my windcheater to the park

Then it began to rain.

Wednesday

It rained all day.

Ava's umbrella had a hole in it.

Thursday

I expected it to rain.

The sun came out instead.

Friday

The weather has gone mad.

I give up!

Chapter 3
Flakes

Saturday

I stayed inside all day.

(later on)

Then something amazing happened.

Sunday

It snowed!

I love the weather!

Questions

Why is Farah unhappy with the weather?

What is wrong with Ava's umbrella?

Name the different types of weather in the story.

What do you do when it snows?